Mandy
FOR GIRLS 1992

PICTURE-STORIES

STORIES TO READ

Printed and published in Great Britain by D.C. THOMSON & CO., LTD.,
185 Fleet Street, London EC4A 2HS. © D.C. THOMSON & CO., LTD., 1991.

ISBN 0-85116-508-7

THE RED BOX OF DESTINY

PART 1

THE old-fashioned red telephone box, on the corner of the High Street, had sent and received many calls in its lifetime — some of joy, and others of great sadness.

Carrie Freeman was waiting for a call that would bring just a little sunshine into her otherwise grey life.

Please ring — it will be so nice to hear a friendly voice.

A friendly voice was sadly lacking in Carrie's life. She lived with her guardians, Aunt Edna and Uncle Pete, and their two children, Amy and Ricky—

HEY! There's no more cereal left, Mum.

Carrie, why didn't you make sure there were enough corn flakes?

I thought there would be enough for today. Ricky's had two bowlfuls.

And why shouldn't I?

Yes, why shouldn't he?

No more of your lip! You ought to be grateful we took you in, after your parents died in that car crash.

4

5

I wanted something to go with this dress.

Please, Amy — give it to me! It's all I've got left from Mum and Dad.

A spark of defiance flared up in Carrie.

It was the last birthday present I had before they died. Give it back, Amy Gregg!

MUM! DAD! Carrie's attacking me!

She went for me, just because I've got her stupid necklace!

C'mere, you little monster!

After a careful beating — where the bruises wouldn't show — Carrie was sent to her room.

No one cares about me — no one.

Aunt Edna and Uncle Pete only took me in because Mum and Dad had an insurance policy — but when they'd squandered the money, they just turned me into a skivvy.

Soon—

I daren't give you any of the family's steak — but you're welcome to my cheap mince, pup.

But then —

What do you think you're doing with that mongrel?

U-Uncle Pete! I didn't think you'd be back so soon.

What's that thing doing in here?

Please don't hurt him. I — I'll take him to the Dog Shelter, right away.

No, Carrie. Wouldn't you like to keep him?

EH?

KEEP HIM?

He'll have to be fed out of your food of course — and you'll have to be completely responsible for him.

I can keep him — really?

I didn't like the way she stood up to Amy over the locket before — but now she loves that fleabag of a dog. She'll toe the line — or else the mutt suffers!

Upstairs, Carrie realised how she had been tricked.

Oh, Jasper — I wish I'd taken you away from here, before I grew to love you. The family will never let you go, now they know how much I care.

Even at school Carrie was a loner. Amy had made the other girls believe Carrie preferred her own company.

No use asking you to join us for the lunchtime record session, Carrie?

Er — no thanks, Amy.

A few minutes later—

Excuse me, I'm new this term. Can you show me where form room 2A is, please? I'm Jilly Baker.

I'm Carrie Freeman. I'll take you.

We've just moved into Brenton. Where do you live, Carrie?

A couple of miles the other way.

I'm an only child. Have you any brothers or sisters?

No. I'm an orphan. But — but I'm very happy with my aunt, uncle and cousins.

That's nice — that you have someone to care, I mean.

If I dared tell her the truth, and the Greggs found out, I know Jasper would suffer.

Carrie got on well with Jilly, but was careful not to let Amy know. And she realised that their friendship could only be at school.

Carrie! Carrie!

Why didn't you go home with Amy and your uncle?

Oh — I felt like a walk, but I didn't know it was going to rain so heavily.

I'll run you home in the car.

Oh, no thanks. I've some shopping to do first, anyway. I must go.

I'll give you a ring tomorrow, as it's Saturday. What's your phone number?

I don't know about that. You — you see, Uncle does a lot of — er — business on Saturdays, and he uses the telephone a lot. He won't want me yattering on!

But suddenly, Carrie felt the need of a friendly voice over the weekend.

Uncle lets me take calls between twelve and quarter past. Perhaps you could give me a ring then?

Fine — write down your number, Carrie.

It's a good job I remembered the number of the phone in the High Street call box. I collect the family's fish and chips on a Saturday, so I can take Jilly's call then.

So on Saturday, Carrie eagerly took Jilly's phone call.

Sorry I'm late ringing. Mum was wondering whether you'd like to come to tea tomorrow? She'll collect you, and drive you back home again.

Oh, er — I'm so sorry, but we're all going out for the day. It's been planned for ages.

Oh, well — perhaps next week?

Um, maybe. I'm sorry, I'll have to hang up now — Uncle wants to use our phone. Bye, Jilly.

Twenty minutes later—

I'm sorry — there was a long queue at the chip shop.

You dawdled on the way home, more like. Get out of the way, mutt!

YELP!

Minutes later—

I don't mind them not giving ME any food, but it breaks my heart to see them do the same to Jasper — and it's my fault, because I spent time talking to Jilly. Perhaps I shouldn't take any more calls from her at the phone box — even if it means losing the only friend I have.

CONTINUED ON PAGE 49

Mum's Secret

SATURDAY morning and Jane Foreman was busy with some homework.

I'll be back about five.

Dinner's at six-thirty, Robert.

Bye, Dad!

Now, my essay — "Our Happy Family". How will I start?

Jane, I'm just going to the shop for some butter.

Okay, Mum!

I'll say "The three people in our family — Mum, Dad and myself — are terrifically happy. The reason —"

I'll work better with a snack. Oh! There's PLENTY of butter. I'll call Mum back.

Mum's gone in the OPPOSITE direction from the shop! A new man's just moved in there — what can she want at HIS house?

"— love and trust. We have no secrets —". Why didn't Mum SAY where she was going?

On Sunday—

Shan't leave you alone for long, love. I'm just going to see Mrs Graham.

Okay, Mum — bye.

But Mrs Graham always visits her sister on Sunday. THIS time I'm going to follow Mum.

Amanda — I'm beginning to feel I've known you for years.

Hello, Derek. I'm running out of excuses to get away to see you. I hope Robert and Jane don't suspect anything.

They hardly know one another, yet it doesn't sound like it. Mum's deliberately lying to me AND Dad!

Monday—

Mrs Jones, can you tell me who's moved into the cottage up the lane from my house?

His name's Mr Lomax, Jane. He's SO handsome and charming, isn't he? Divorced too. What makes you ask, dear?

Oh — er — just curiosity.

He can't have charmed *MY MUM*, can he?

On Wednesday, at school in the nearby town—

— and have you seen that Mr Lomax from London? I heard my Mum say she thinks he's a real hunk!

I bet he'll soon be chatting up all the good-looking women in our village!

Look at poor Fiona Wood. She's so miserable these days — ever since her Mum ran off with a divorced man.

That couldn't happen to *ME* — could it?

You and Mum never seem to go out *TOGETHER* these days.

We have our different interests, pet. I have my golf, and your Mum her Women's Institute — like tonight.

Oh, poor Dad — he doesn't suspect a thing. But — is Mum *REALLY* at her meeting, or —

Thursday—

It's Dad's birthday on Saturday. I want an extra-nice card for him.

— and I tell you, Maisie — that Mr Lomax, they say he has a special way with women. Well, there are plenty pretty girls right here in our village.

VALDA
and the Burning of Barthol

IT was Gala Day when Valda, girl of mystery, entered the village of New Barthol.

I am needed in this village. I felt the call — and now I know that I have reached my destination.

Burn Bartholomew! Burn him! Burn him!

Whose effigy is this, that causes the people of Barthol to bay like bloodthirsty animals — save for that one child?

That's what we think of YOUR family in this village, Sarah Bartholomew!

18

Do you not wish to join in, Sarah?

My friends have all turned against me, since the Professor uncovered the forgotten legend of the Burning of Barthol. They say my ancestor burned their families out of their homes, and they hardly speak to me any more.

Stop, my friends! Follow me, and I will show you a greater treasure than that which you hunt.

Take no notice. She's only a visitor. What does *SHE* know about our village?

Valda fixed the young man in a penetrating stare —

You will come with *ME*, Eric Joyner — and the rest will follow.

Yes — we will come.

Valda led the villagers of Barthol over the bridge to the ruined castle. There —

Under here you will find a ringed stone, which you must raise to find the treasure we seek.

The ground was cleared — and the stone was found!

I — I can't lift this stone. I bet it hasn't been disturbed for centuries.

You are correct. It has not been moved for more than three centuries. I will do it.

She lifted the stone as if it weighed nothing at all!

There's a vault underneath! Nobody in the village knew of it — how could *SHE* know?

19

"At last, in the rays of the setting sun —"

The stranger has a helping hand for all who need it!

Is the sun playing tricks, making shadows? The stranger seems no longer a young girl —

"Then the stranger did take a crystal from a pouch at her waist, and held it up to the sun."

We cannot face this fierce glow — yet *SHE* bathes in it!

"Our community worked to build a new settlement."

For a moment, I thought you were old, but you *ARE* just a slip of a girl. My eyes deceived me.

No doubt, good friend.

"Then the wolves did come, as the villagers had feared."

Stop! Do not attack these creatures. They are not your natural enemies — it is *YOU* who are *THEIRS!*

Go in peace, wild ones. These people mean you no harm — and the rest of the forest is yours.

Who is this girl who can speak to wolves, and have them do her bidding?

23

DOWN WITH BOYS!

BEST friends Jane Bell and Polly Bruce had made a vow to keep off boys — for GOOD!

Valentine's Day is coming up, Polly. If we get any Valentines from stupid boys, we'll rip them up!

Too true, Jane. We won't send any, either. I can think of better things to spend my money on —

— like sweets! Let's go in here — I want to buy some from the pic-n-mix, to eat in double history this afternoon.

Okay, Polly.

But, soon after—

Fifty-five pence, please —

Oh! I've only got forty. Can you lend me fifteen, Jane?

Sorry — I'm skint. You'll just have to put some sweets back —

Hang on, Polly. I'll pay the extra.

Oh — thanks, Neil!

Neil Rivers is in our class at school. I suppose it IS nice of him to come to Polly's rescue.

But, to Jane's annoyance—

Have some sweets, Neil. You helped to buy them, after all.

I'll share sweets with you any time, Polly.

I don't believe this! They're chatting each other up! I'll have to talk to Polly, and remind her of our vow.

But—

What vow? Have a sweet and stop lecturing me, Jane. Neil obviously fancies me, and I think he's dead nice, too — so we'll probably go out on a date, soon.

Not if I can help it! Boys are nothing but trouble.

Next morning—

HUH! Polly didn't call for me this morning, and now I know why! There's the sneaky toad — catching the bus without me, so she can chat up Neil Rivers again — he gets our bus. I'll definitely need to put him *OFF* Polly!

Later, at school—

I think you should know, Neil — Polly is *ALWAYS* up to her sly little trick at the pic-n-mix. She takes more sweets than she can afford, then waits for someone else to stump up — like you did, yesterday!

Don't believe her, Neil!

Don't worry, Polly — I don't! Polly paid my bus-fare this morning, to make up. So I definitely wouldn't class her as a scrounger, Jane!

Huh! So much for making him go off Polly! He still seems to fancy her — and it's disgraceful the way she's lapping up his attention!

But later—

Blank page, Jane? You were supposed to do the maths problems I set you at the start of the period.

I know, sir — but I didn't know how to work them out.

Cheer up, Jane — they're quite easy, once you get the hang of them. Listen, I'll come round to your house tonight and explain the maths to you, if you like.

Thanks, Neil — that would be great!

The crafty sneak — so SHE'S after Neil! I'll have to nip this in the bud!

And so—

I think you should know this, Neil. Jane's parents don't like her asking boys to the house. You won't be made at all welcome — so I wouldn't go, if I were you.

I won't then, Polly — thanks for the tip-off.

But, that evening—

Hi, Polly — I thought you might like to know the result of you warning Neil not to come to my house. He asked me round to HIS, instead — and that's where I'm going now. We should get really cosy over the maths books!

I'm disgusted with you, Jane Bell. Doesn't the vow we made mean anything to you?

As little as it means to YOU, Polly Bruce. What's really bugging you is that Neil Rivers is interested in ME now — and I fancy HIM!

Huh! He's only helping you with your maths because he's taken pity on a thicko! I'm the one he's REALLY keen on!

A few days later—

I'll buy a Valentine for Neil. Oh, there's Jane coming out of the card shop.

Hi, Jane — is that a Valentine card for Neil you've been buying? Let's see it, then!

No chance — mind your own business, Polly!

Be like that, then!

I know how to find out which card Jane bought.

And, in the shop—

Excuse me. My friend has just left, with a Valentine card I really like — but I don't see it any place. Can you show me where she got it?

I remember it. Let me show you —

So this is it. But now I know, I'll buy a much BIGGER one for Neil, to out-do Jane's!

And, at school—

I used my brains to find out which card YOU got for Neil, then I bought one twice the size! This will make yours look like a cheap, grotty little affair!

I'm not bothered. It's what's ON the card that counts, not the size of it!

28

But, after school—

I know how to make Neil lose interest in Polly, once and for all. I'll buy half a dozen cheapie Valentines, cover them with sloppy verses — and add Polly's signature!

And, the day before Valentine's Day—

That's them posted, to six other boys in our class! I'm not posting my card to Neil yet, because there's another verse I want to write on it. I'll do it in school this afternoon.

And, after school—

I've got hockey practice, Anna — so could you post this for me?

Okay, Jane.

I'LL post Jane's Valentine, Anna — I go right past the post-box and I've one of my own to post, anyway.

All right — I don't suppose Jane cares who posts it, as long as it gets there.

But, soon after—

I've posted mine to Neil — but I'll stick Jane's one in this bin. Now he won't even GET her measly little Valentine! I hope he sends me one, too — and not HER!

29

There's no Valentine from Neil. I can't help feeling disappointed.

Jane hadn't got one, either.

I'm not surprised. Did you think he'd waste his money on *YOU*?

Well, *YOU* certainly wasted your money, with that outsize card. He obviously doesn't care about you, or he'd have sent one in return. Anyway, I'm sure he likes the small, *TASTEFUL* card I sent!

At school, to Jane's fury—

Thanks for the card, Polly. It's really nice!

Glad you liked it, Neil.

Did you like *MINE*?

Eh? Sorry, Jane — but I didn't *GET* a card from you! Are you sure you sent me one?

Positive. It must have got lost in the post, or something.

No, it didn't. *I* posted it, instead of Anna — in a litter bin!

You rotten, mean pig! But you needn't look so smug, because *YOU'RE* in for a surprise, as well!

And minutes later—

Thanks for my Valentine, Polly —

WHAT?

Yeah! And mine!

And mine!

You seem to have sent quite a few, Polly!

Our Polly's a downright flirt, Neil. She fancies half the boys in the class!

But — but I *DIDN'T* send them Valentines —

I did — in your name! Neil's bound to go off you now — he won't fancy a boy-chaser!

Of all the dirty rotten tricks! I'm glad I dumped *YOUR* Valentine card — Neil probably thinks you lied about sending him one, so he won't be keen on you now, *EITHER*!

But, to both girls' surprise—

How would you both like to come to our Football Club Valentine Disco, tonight? Come really early, if you can make it.

I'll be there, Neil!

And me!

It's obvious he still likes me, despite your lowdown scheming. Pity he asked you to the disco as well — but I suppose he felt he *HAD* to, as you're my friend.

You mean, he felt he had to ask *YOU*, big-head! It's me he's *REALLY* after — you'll see!

And that night—

I can't think why you bothered to come early. Neil won't even look in your direction.

That's what *YOU* think! Once Neil sees me, you'll fade into the woodwork!

31

Then, inside—

Hi, Jane and Polly — glad you could come early. Listen, I'm in charge of the buffet for tonight, but I have to go somewhere. Could you two start putting the stuff out? I won't be long.

Er, yes —

No problem, Neil.

An hour later—

That's the food all ready, though Neil isn't back yet. It's a bit of a cheek, leaving us to do it all. But I suppose he'll make up for it, by dancing with me all night!

If he can stop dancing with ME long enough, that is!

But there was a shock in store for Jane and Polly!

This is my girlfriend, Angela. Sorry I've been so long, Jane and Polly — but she wasn't ready.

I don't believe this!

Of all the cheek!

Thanks for being such a help, girls. You'll be staying for the disco?

No, thanks. We've got better things to do with our time.

What a couple of mugs we've been, Jane. We both thought Neil Rivers fancied us — but all the time he was only being nice, so we'd do his slaving at his precious disco! What a conniving creep —

— just like the rest of the male species! But I suppose it serves us right for breaking our vow. From now on, it's definitely 'Down With Boys'!

THE END

32

LOSING LUCY

I'VE always liked swimming. My season ticket to our local swimming baths is usually dog-eared and grubby with use. Not that I'm anything brilliant in the water. But I'm quite happy with my modest few lengths of the pool.

My best friend Lucy, however, didn't share my enthusiasm. She couldn't swim a stroke — and, to be honest, she couldn't be bothered to learn. It was too much hassle to get herself down to the swimming baths. Anyway, Lucy was dead fussy about her hair, so she hated the water messing it up. She used to go, once in a blue moon, to please me — but then she'd stand, shivering, in the shallow end of the pool, as if she was firmly rooted to the tiled bottom.

"I'm freezing," she'd moan.

"That's because you're not moving about," I'd tell her. "Honestly, Lucy — a dead fish has more life than you. Try to swim, for any sake!" But, next thing I knew, Lucy would sneak out, to spend the rest of the time skulking in the hot showers!

"Phew — torture over," she'd giggle, as we went home, later. "I don't know what you see in swimming, Carol — it leaves me cold, wet, and bored!"

"Well, everyone to their own taste," I'd tell her. I wished Lucy was into swimming, too — but I didn't really mind that she wasn't! After all, there were lots of other things we did together.

Then, one Monday, we had a holiday from school.

"Fancy the baths?" I asked Lucy. I knew she'd say "no," and she did.

"I'd rather go to the fair," she told me eagerly. "It's only here for two weeks, and you can go swimming ANY time!"

"Okay!" I grinned. Fair was fair, and all that! To be honest, I can't stand fairs, with all the accompanying hoo-ha, and racket. But Lucy loved them. So, if she endured the baths on occasion with ME, it was only right I should go to the fair with HER!

So, that Monday afternoon found us wandering around the stalls, trying to get candy floss into our mouths, and not on other people. (Who invented that stuff, anyway?)

"Oh, look!" screeched Lucy, pointing to a monstrosity which looked like a purple octopus straight out of science fiction. "There's the Thrill-spiller! Let's go on it!"

"Not on your life," I shuddered. "But don't let me stop YOU having the pleasure!"

"See you!" yelled Lucy. She shot off to queue with other idiots willing to pay for an upside-down horror experience, and I wandered on, looking for something to do while waiting for her.

The truth is, I'm scared to go on any ride that turns you up, down, round, over, inside-out or what have you — and I'm a real dumbo, when it comes to things like hoopla, and coconut shies. So, when I spotted a fortune teller's tent, I wandered in, to have my fortune told. It would be something to giggle about with Lucy, later.

But it turned out to be anything BUT funny! Madame Fortuna peered into the proverbial glass ball, and told me that I had a bright future. I could have told her that, as I'm pretty brainy! (Says me, modestly!) Then she informed me I would have problems with a small, dark person! So what's new, I thought. That would be my little brother, Paul, who was a pain in the neck. But then she told me something that turned me icy cold, all over — though it was warm in the tent.

"You will lose your best friend to the water," she said.

I only had one best friend, and that was Lucy! Did Madame Fortuna's words mean she was going to DROWN?

"What else COULD they mean?" I thought, with a shiver. And Lucy couldn't swim, which made the prospect all the more likely!

I was worried sick, as I made my way out again into the sunlight. I couldn't BEAR the thought of losing Lucy like that. Of course, I didn't say anything to HER about it. But I made up my mind about one thing. I just HAD to get Lucy swimming. Then, and only then, would there be little chance of that dreadful prophecy coming true.

I knew if I suggested to Lucy, straight out, that she learn to swim, I'd get the usual negative response. So I had to resort to more devious methods. And a couple of days later, at school, I heard Gary Lester — a boy Lucy had fancied for ages — telling his mate he was going to the baths that night. So I hastened to tell Lucy.

"It could have been the perfect chance for you to chat up Gary," I said slyly. "Pity you never go to the baths."

"Well, I might make tonight the exception," laughed Lucy, with a gleam in her eye.

"Good," I said casually. "As it happens, I'm going tonight too — so meet me outside the swimming baths, at seven."

I felt dead pleased with myself, as I ate my tea that night. Lucy was going to the baths, which was half the battle. The other half was persuading her to learn to swim — which shouldn't be too difficult, if GARY offered

33

to coach her! I decided to drop a word in his ear, if I could.

But I was in for a let-down. Lucy was outside the baths, all right — but she was all dressed up like she was going to a disco. And what was worse, she'd no swimming stuff with her!

"I didn't bring it," she explained, cheerfully. "I'm not going into the pool. I thought I'd just park myself on the front seats of the spectators' area. I can still talk to Gary, from there — even if he's in the pool!" And that's what she did. Gary was in and out of the water, like a hot potato — or a WET potato, rather — hanging over the barrier, to chat up Lucy. So much for her first swimming lesson, I thought, as I swam around, disgruntled, on my own. I'd have to try some other tactic.

Luckily, I had another idea up my sleeve. And the following Saturday morning, I toddled round to my Aunt Jackie's house. She has three-year-old twins, Sam and Susie — so she's permanently harassed. She was over the moon when I offered to take them to the toddlers' pool at the swimming baths, and she got them ready like greased lightning, in case I changed my mind.

"I'll get my friend, Lucy, to come too — so we can look after one of them each," I told Aunt Jackie. "She won't mind!" Lucy has always said she fancied the toddlers' pool, because it was warm — and shallow, so the water was far away from her hair. She liked kids, too — so there was no problem!

"Hang on and I'll grab my gear," she grinned.

"I suppose Sam and Susie are pretty timid in the water," she mused as we went into the baths.

"Well, not exactly," I murmured. You see, I was employing shock tactics this time. I didn't tell Lucy that the twins were competent little swimmers. And when she saw the pair of them threshing across the toddlers' pool, her jaw dropped.

"They're actually SWIMMING!" she gasped.

"Can YOU swim, Lucy?" asked Sam, when they'd swum back again.

"No, she can't!" I giggled.

"But I'm definitely going to learn, NOW!" mumbled Lucy.

"Good — you can't let a couple of three-year-olds beat you, can you?" I grinned. I'd wanted to shame Lucy

into learning, and it looked like I'd succeeded! Striking while the iron was hot, I suggested we return to the baths on Monday night, so I could show her the basics!

"Fine by me," said Lucy.

So on Monday night, I had her doing the correct leg and arm movements, while I held her chin. Lucy now seemed dead keen to learn, and she progressed rapidly. A couple of weeks later, she was off on her own, doing a reasonable breast stroke — and soon she was coping with one breadth of the pool, then two. Then came the day she managed a whole length!

I must admit I was surprised at how good Lucy was, in the water. Even as a beginner, she had a style and class about her swimming that I'd never had. She was soon able to out-strip me, and I didn't have to twist her arm to go to the baths any more, either. She was keener than me — and she'd go on her own, if I couldn't make it!

One night, a couple of months later, I'd to visit my Gran in hospital, so I had to give the baths a miss. But Lucy went — and next day, at school, she had some exciting news. She told me that a man at the side of the pool had been watching her swimming. Then he'd called her over, and told her he was Mr Thomson, a talent scout for the Dolphin Swimming Club. He'd asked Lucy if she'd like to join, and train with them.

"The Dolphins!" I gasped, amazed. "But they're the top club, Lucy! He must have been really impressed by your swimming!"

"I suppose he must have been," giggled Lucy. "Mum and Dad say I CAN join, if it's what I want — and it IS what I want. I never thought it would happen, but swimming's become dead important to me. The thing is, though — it means being really dedicated — you know, training in the early mornings, and every night — so we wouldn't see so much of each other."

"Oh, well — that can't be helped," I said, casually. "If it's what you want, go for it!" But inside, I was feeling miserable. Were all the great times we'd had together, about to fly out the window? I told myself that I'd still see Lucy at weekends, but it was a vain hope. Lucy began to train then — and I ended up only seeing her at school. Even there, all she talked about was swimming!

It was about that time when I became friendly with a girl in our class, called Sharon. She was really nice — though I secretly knew she could never match up to Lucy. She was an average swimmer too, like me — so we sometimes went to the baths together. We never saw Lucy there, though — because the Dolphins had their own training times — and anyway, they used the special competition pool, next door.

Some time later, Lucy was competing in her first big inter-club gala. So Sharon and I went to cheer her on. She gave us a casual wave, as she ran past us in her smart Dolphin swimsuit, to line up at the start of a race. Sharon must have noticed the bleak look on my face.

"You used to be such good friends with Lucy," she said, touching my arm. "But you hardly ever see her these days, now she's got the swimming bug. It looks like you've lost her to the water!"

For a moment, I was back in that musty tent, hearing Madame Fortuna say the same words. And I suddenly realised that her prophecy HAD come true. I HAD lost Lucy to the water — though not in the terrible way I'd feared. As I watched her forge confidently ahead of her rivals, I felt a sadness as deep as the deep end of the swimming pool, about our lost friendship. But I wished her all the best.

THE END

WHO IS *SYLVIE*?

A NEW girl joined Rachel Hunt's class at Woodhill School —

This is Sylvie Roberts, class. I hope you'll do all you can to make her welcome. Sit next to Rachel, Sylvie.

She looks okay — I'm sure we'll get on.

At break —

Sylvie, meet Paula and Deb. We go around together — join us if you like.

Thanks! It's awful when you don't know anyone.

Where was your last school, Sylvie?

Oh — at Camford. It's miles away.

That's funny! My cousin Rebecca lives at Camford — and she has to bus out to Donbury, cos Camford Secondary was closed down.

Perhaps you know my cousin — Rebecca Hunt?

No — er — I went to a private school. Er, what's on the timetable this afternoon?

It'll be music and movement in place of swimming, worse luck. I hope the pool will be back in use soon — it's having some repairs done.

Oh, great! I love music and movement — it's almost like dancing!

That afternoon —

Very good, Sylvie. I can see you'll be an asset to us. The rest of you must try harder — I want a first-class team for our display, later this term.

Sylvie *IS* good — she'll be in the team for sure.

On the way home —

This is where I live with my aunt. My parents are abroad just now.

I live round the corner in Elm Drive. You must come to tea soon, Sylvie.

Thanks, I'd like that, Rachel. But — er — Auntie's not keen on having *MY* friends in. She's not used to it, you see.

Oh, that's okay, Sylvie.

Poor thing! It must be lonely for her.

Sylvie doesn't talk much about herself. It's odd, but I've got this feeling I've seen her before somewhere. But — where could it have been?

Next day, as Sylvie came into the cloakroom —

There are some workmen at the pool. I really miss swimming — will we go to the Lido after school? We can take Sylvie as well.

I keep thinking I've seen Sylvie before. She looks sort of familiar.

That's just what I thought! Hey, Sylvie — did you live here, before you moved to Camford?

No! I've lived all over the place. Dad's in the army, you see. That's why I'm with my aunt now — it's more settled.

That still doesn't explain where I've seen Sylvie —

Did someone mention the Lido? You can count me in — I love swimming!

The following week —

Unfortunately the school swimming pool needs major repairs, and the County Council cannot find the money for at least two years.

That's awful! Woodhill without a pool is like fish without chips!

The Governors are, therefore, hoping that we can raise the money ourselves. Please consider carefully how we may best do this.

Hey — we can have a disco!

And jumble sales — it's about time Paula had some new clothes!

Watch it, you!

In class, the girls gave their ideas to Miss Smythe.

All these ideas must become workable schemes, with proper plans made. In the meantime, schoolwork must come first.

And it's choir this afternoon. Mrs Milton thinks I've got a voice like a foghorn.

Well, Rachel — she's dead right!

37

During music —

♪ Nymphs and shepherds come away — ♪

Sylvie's got a super voice. She makes me sound like a pig at feeding time.

Lovely — and we have a new voice among us. I'd like to hear Sylvie Roberts singing solo, please.

♪ In this grove, let's dance and play — ♪

Delightful! Has your voice been trained, Sylvie?

I've had — well — a few singing lessons.

Mrs Milton — would you help us to organise a concert in aid of the pool? Sylvie could sing, and we'll back her in some of the numbers.

But —

No! No — I CAN'T sing in public!

It's for our pool, Sylvie! You love swimming, and you sure know how to use the old vocal chords!

I'm sorry — I just CAN'T!

Huh — that's a fat lot of use!

May I remind you that the money-raising activities are VOLUNTARY! No one is to be forced into helping.

Later, at netball practice —

Mrs Jones has asked me to be in the music and movement display team. I'm quite looking forward to it!

So Sylvie's prepared to do that! It's funny she won't SING in public, though!

The practice began —

Well done, Val!

Val should make the junior team at this rate. I hope I do too.

Later —

I'd like you both in the junior team. That means you'll be playing against St Bede's on Saturday week.

WHOOPEE!

I'm sorry — it's my sister's birthday that day, Mrs Jones, and we're all going out.

Loyalty to the school is important, Val. If you're in the team — surely that should come first!

Phew, she's really laying it on thick! I'm glad I can make the St Bede's match!

Then, a few days later —

Our music and movement display has been fixed for the week after half-term, so you must all work really hard.

Er, Mrs Jones — could I have a word, please?

I'm afraid I won't be able to make the display after all, Mrs Jones. I — er — have other commitments.

That's a blow, Sylvie. I was banking on you. I'll have to ask Sonia Jenkins to take your place.

I don't believe it! Jonesy did her nut when Val skipped the St Bede's match — yet Sylvie's let off the display without a murmur! It's ODD!

The evening of the jumble sale —

JUMBLE SALE

I want a photo of the helpers. Gather round, you lot!

Oh, I must get a hanky. Carry on without me!

It's almost as though Sylvie doesn't WANT her photo taken.

Okay, Sylvie — I'll take another one now — oh, too late! The big spenders are here!

I'm sure Sylvie kept out of the way deliberately!

How about this for the disco, Paula? You'd look fabby — and when you're tired of it, we'll use it as a tent!

I wouldn't be seen dead in one of YOUR grotty cast-offs, Deb — though it was kind of you to donate it!

This is a brilliant way of raising money, Deb!

Yeah! More fun than a jumble sale! Sylvie looks fantastic, doesn't she? Wish I could afford a dress like that.

This is ace! You're a great dancer, Sylvie!

You're not too bad yourself, Roy.

The pair-dancing contest is next, Sylvie. The others won't stand a chance if we enter.

Okay, Roy — it'll be a laugh, anyway.

A photographer from the local paper is here — ready to snap the winning couple. We could be famous!

Gosh, is that the time? I'll have to go — my aunt is a real worrier, and I promised to be back early.

What did I say? Oh, well — I'd better see her home, I suppose.

It's nothing personal, Roy — Sylvie's aunt is very strict.

All the same — it was a bit sudden. Sylvie seems to be very camera-shy.

On Monday, at school —

We've raised a fair bit for the pool so far.

We need heaps more, though — and I'm exhausted already.

Yeah — I'm going to have a sponsored sleep, right through half-term!

No, you're not! We're going to show Sylvie round our favourite haunts.

Oh, I won't be able to come. I'll be — visiting the family.

Oh — shame!

That reminds me. I must phone my cousin Rebecca some time.

During half-term —

It's Sylvie!

Crumbs! She must have posh relations, if they send her home in a limousine!

There's something funny about Sylvie. Have you noticed how she won't have her photo taken? She says her parents are abroad — but I'm wondering if they're in prison!

What makes you say THAT, Rachel?

If they're notorious criminals, there was probably a photo of the whole family in the papers — and Sylvie doesn't want to be recognised.

Come off it, Rachel! That's a bit strong!

She's probably been visiting them over half-term — and the chauffeur is paid for out of their ill-gotten gains!

Stop it, Rachel! I've never heard such a load of rubbish — you've been watching too many crime films on TV!

But that evening, Rachel phoned her cousin —

No, there's no private school here in Camford, Rachel. And I've never heard of any Sylvie Roberts. What makes you ask?

Sylvie is a bit of a mystery, Rebecca. I'm just checking up on her — but nothing adds up, so far!

Next day —

There's a girl at Sylvie's house —

Louise! It's lovely to see you! Come in — I'm longing to hear all your news!

Huh! I thought Sylvie's aunt didn't like her friends visiting? There IS something funny going on, whatever Paula and Deb say!

Next day, at Rachel's house —

It's time for "Docksiders".

It's the best soap on telly, these days.

That Dinah is a scream!

Yes, Cheryl Robinson — the actress who plays her — is great in the part.

Watching the series every week, it makes you think you really KNOW Dinah — doesn't it?

Hey, Rachel — there's your phone ringing.

43

Sylvie? Yes, Deb and Paula are here — what, you want us to come to your aunt's house, right away?

That's a surprise! Let's go —

An even bigger surprise was waiting!

Hi, girls!

DINAH!

Well, not really —

SYLVIE? Cheryl Robinson?

Right both times, Rachel! Come in, and I'll explain.

Cheryl explained that she had become weary of her off-screen life at a stage school. She wanted to be an ordinary schoolgirl — enjoying ordinary friendships with other girls, instead of the admiration of fans. So she persuaded her parents to let her live for a term with her aunt, as Sylvie Roberts.

Auntie's so proud of me, and she has all these photos. So I couldn't have visitors, except my friend Louise from stage school. The staff at Woodhill knew — that's why Mrs Jones let me off the display to go to the studios. And I said I came from Camford — the first name that came into my head.

My contract doesn't allow me to perform in public without permission. But I've been speaking to my agent, and now I've come out into the open.

Why? Don't keep us in suspense, Sylvie — er, Cheryl!

He's agreed I can organise a charity concert in aid of the pool, and ask all my friends in showbiz to take part.

Oh, that'd be *MAGIC!*

So —

A Docksider just like me, I'm sure you'll all agree —

Sylvie looks quite different with that wig. And she's brilliant — the audience loves her!

Meeting all the stars has been like a dream come true. I never thought I'd have so many famous names in my autograph book!

Ken Kenton gave me a kiss, when he signed mine! I'm not going to wash my face for a week!

The following week —

It's great that the concert raised enough money for the new swimming pool, Sylvie.

And it's great to know that I've got *REAL* friends in the *REAL* world! Now — off we go to visit the studios, girls.

So be extra nice to that new girl at school — you never know who she may be! You could even end up with a television star for your best friend — like Paula, Deb and me!

No. But Anna Petrova, the famous ballerina, is prepared to take Kelly as a private pupil. She does so only because she believes Kelly has a great future in ballet.

Later that evening —

The fees are much higher than I expected. It's going to be a real struggle —

Please, Dad. I'll do anything I can to earn extra money.

If I do some extra overtime at the factory, and Mum does extra hours at the supermarket — I reckon we'll just about do it!

Oh, thank you — thank you!

It was a struggle to pay Kelly's fees, but her parents knew that one day their sacrifices would be worth it.

Your new ballet shoes, Kelly.

Thanks, Mum.

I know you wanted a new dress, Mum. When I'm rich and famous, I'll buy you a whole wardrobe full!

Just be happy, Kelly.

One evening, Anna Petrova called to see Kelly's parents.

You have heard of Belmont Grange, the world-famous ballet school? They are holding entrance examinations next month, for two places. I think Kelly has a very good chance of being accepted.

I'm going to be honest — our finances are stretched to the limit, even now.

51

But Kelly was wound up with a mixture of nervousness and excitement.

What if we get a puncture? They won't wait, and I'll lose my big chance. Hurry, Dad!

Kelly, stop panicking! I'm trying to concentrate.

Dad, if we take that turning —

KELLY!

For a split second Dad lost his concentration, and that's all it took —

A few days later —

The tests are conclusive, I'm afraid. Kelly's legs were badly broken in the accident. She'll be able to walk, but only with the use of sticks.

But her dancing —

I'm so very sorry. Those days are over.

It'll break her heart.

Kelly was devastated.

"No, no — it's not true! You're lying!"

"Kelly, I'm so sorry."

"It was *YOUR* fault! You were driving — you've ruined my life!"

Kelly became embittered, blaming her parents for the accident.

"I'm thirsty, Mum. Can I have some orange, please?"

"Yes, of course, love. It's in the fridge."

"*I* can't get it — *I* can't carry it, using two sticks!"

"All right, dear. I'll go."

"Dr Marsh has called to see how you're getting on, Kelly."

"Oh, wonderfully! I'm entering the London Marathon next year, didn't you know?"

Kelly! Sorry, Dr Marsh.

It's all right. Perhaps Kelly and I could have a little chat?

Your Dad tells me you can walk quite well now.

Oh, yes — with two sticks. That's great, huh!

Kelly, self-pity is very destructive. I know how you must feel, but —

How CAN you know? You're not a cripple. Did your parents ruin YOUR life? GO AWAY!

Kelly's still upset, but I don't think it's helping by letting her blame you entirely.

But I was driving. I shouldn't have lost concentration. I know you mean well, Doctor, but I think you'd better go.

Come along, love. Let's go inside. Perhaps you'd like to watch TV?

At least I'm capable of THAT.

But —

How could you be so cruel, putting THIS on?

We didn't know, love — really.

CONTINUED ON PAGE 73

The Lucky Locket

CHARLOTTE had spent her life in an orphanage, but now it was time for her to leave.

Matron says I'm to be scullery-maid at Gravely Hall, Harriet. But I'll miss you, after all these years here.

You've bin a good lass, Charlotte — and didn't I always say yer was special?

Yes, you used to say, 'yer never know wiv an orphan' — as if I might be a princess or sumfink!

Heh, heh — well yer never DO know! Now, where is it?

A locket! I never seen anyfink so beautiful! Where did you get it, Harriet?

It's yourn, m'lovely! I found it tucked in yer shawl the night I brung yer in, off the steps. That an' a bit o' paper tellin' your name — Charlotte.

56

I had a mind to sell it — but I've done all right workin' here, and now I'm gittin' to the end of me time. Now yer must 'ave it back. Don't sell it till yer desperate, mind!

Oh, I won't EVER sell it, Harriet — it's far too precious.

This must be my muvver — same dark hair and eyes as me. Why did you leave me, Muvver, and where are you now? I wish you was here — I'm so afraid.

Next day —

Coo! What a luvverly big place! Perhaps I'll be 'appy here, after all — an' I've got me locket to bring me luck.

Here is your new scullery-maid, Cook.

Thanks, Miss Murdoch — hope she lasts longer than the last runaway brat!

Charlotte was soon hard at work —

After that, Meggie will show you the pails and brushes. I want the scullery floor clean enough to eat orf!

Charlotte's a mighty posh name for a scullery-maid, ain't it? I shall call yer 'Lowly' — cos that's what you are, the lowest of the low! Now — get on with it, Lowly.

Hurry up with that, girl. There's potatoes to peel, and when you've finished those there's plenty more to be done!

That night, in the cold attic room —

Oh, Muvver, I wish you was 'ere to comfort me — I've jest had the worst day of me life! There was hard work to do at the orphanage, but at least Matron was fair, and the kids was mostly nice, and there was Harriet. I'd better hide you away now.

Next day —

Poll's sick, so you've to 'elp me wiv the upstairs fireplaces. Carry these — an' remember, if yer sees any of the gentry, yer bobs a curtsey, and keeps yer eyes down.

Cor! Ain't it beautiful?

Don't stand there an' gawp! Git to work on that fireplace, an' I'll do the lounge — that's where the gentry lounges around, see?

How wonderful to be one of the gentry, 'stead of bein' a servant. I wonder if me muvver was? Perhaps I am as well, by rights.

Butler, we will 'ave the best silver and crystal fer tonight's party — the Prince of Wales is honouring us wiv 'is presence.

Silly baggage, puttin' on airs and graces! Git that fireplace done, double-quick. Wait till I tell the 'ousekeeper about this!

Please don't, Meggie!

But Meggie told all the servants, and —

Careful, Lady Muck! You don't want to get your fine dress dirty!

Yes, yer wants to look yer best fer the Prince tonight — don't yer? Ha-ha!

It was only a bit of fun, Muvver. I was jest imagining what it would be like to be a lady, same as you were. What would they say if I showed them the locket? But that's my secret!

Next day —

Beats me why a fine lady like Miss Charlotte is workin' as a lowly scullery-maid!

Must 'ave fallen on bad times, poor fing! Tee-hee!

When Charlotte could stand no more, she hid in the stables. There —

Hey, what's up? Come on, lass. Fings can't be that bad!

Desperate, Charlotte struggled free.

Gotta get away from them — they **MUSTN'T** get the locket!

You jest wait, Lowly!

Soon —

I seem to 'ave lost 'em, thank goodness. Oh, what a mess I look — still, I must get on wiv it.

Please, sir — what will yer give me fer this? I know it's worf a lot of money.

Hmmmm . . .

Just then —

Grab 'er! Whatever she's got, she must 'ave stole it!

I didn't steal it — it was me muvver's!

This **LADY** — the mother of a dirty urchin such as **YOU**? Save your lies for the law, my girl — go for a policeman, you two!

No, sir, I beg you — I speaks the truth!

Poor Charlotte was taken before a magistrate.

I didn't steal it, sir! You can ask old Harriet, the 'elper at Borton Orphanage, if you don't believe me. She knows all about it.

Hmm! Very well — this case is adjourned, so that this Harriet person can be traced. Take her away.

That night —

What a horrible place. But I shan't 'ave to stay 'ere long, once they've found Harriet to speak fer me.

But, two days later —

Investigations have revealed that the old woman, Harriet, died a few weeks ago. With no evidence to the contrary, the prisoner is found guilty of theft, and shall be jailed.

No! Please no!

After several weeks locked in her miserable cell, Charlotte had given up all hope. Then, one day, a warder took her to a small room, where a lady was waiting.

She was a stranger, and she gazed at Charlotte with eyes full of sadness — and hope. Then she spoke, in a foreign accent.

Please, do not be nervous, ma petite. If I could ask — would you be so kind as to show me your left shoulder?

W-why?

Do as the lady asks, girl!

There it is! Oh, my dear — I think I must tell you a little story. Come, sit down.

The story began in France, twelve years earlier, with a young lady giving her parents some unwelcome news.

You wish to marry my Head Groom? Are you mad, daughter?

Think, Adele! How could you be happy, married to a servant, when you have had the best that life can offer?

I can only be happy with Pierre — riches mean nothing!

That night —

Oh, Pierre — running away will break my parents' hearts.

It is the only way we can be together, my love. We will be safe in England — and after we have been married for a year or two, we will come back. Surely then they will accept what has happened.

In England, Pierre found work in the stables of a big house. Though poor, he and Adele were happy.

I could not be more content, my love.

I believe you will be, husband, when I tell you that I am to have a baby!

But one day —

— the horse reared, and its hoof struck your husband on the side of his head. He died instantly, I'm afraid.

No!

I'm sorry, lass. The master says to give you this money in compensation, but I'm afraid you'll have to leave the cottage by the end of the week.

But, where will I go with my baby? Oh, Pierre — my Pierre!

Poor Adele searched for work, but no one would employ a foreigner with a baby. Soon her money ran out, and she had no choice but to leave her child on the steps of an orphanage.

There, ma petite! You will not be here long, I promise. Soon your Mama will find work, and save enough money to take us to France.

So—

What do I want, more than anything?

MAP READING
1:10560 =
6" to 1

Jenny, stop dreaming and pay attention.

At break—

I know what I really want — it's to be a writer!

And you CAN be! With YOUR powers, you can be anything in the world!

That night, Jenny searched through all her stories.

I think this is the best one I've ever written. It'd be lovely to see it in print.

It's called "The Midnight Mermaid" and I'm going to send it to my favourite mag. But first I need some magic.

It's nearly midnight. You've got to help me, Will — I'll put my story on the floor, and I want you to put your paw on it.

THE MIDNIGHT MERMAID

And as midnight struck—

Midnight — a secret magic time. Magic, please rest on this story of mine.

THE MIDNIGHT MERMAID

I'll seal the envelope quickly, before the magic wears off.

The Editor Mandy

THE RED BOX OF DESTINY

PART 3

RAMA CHAND was nervous, as she went to use the telephone in the old red box —

I'll ring Miss Ainsley now. I want to be a good daughter. I hope I'm making the right choice.

Hello, Miss Ainsley? It's Rama —

Am I doing the right thing?

Rama lived with her widowed father and elder brother above the family's popular restaurant.

I look forward to seeing your smiling face, Rama. It's a pleasure to be served by you.

Thank you, sir. It's my pleasure to serve you.

You are a natural for the family business, Rama.

With me as chef and Rama waitressing, you'll soon be redundant, Dad!

May I finish now, please, Dad? The other girls can manage.

Are you feeling tired, Rama? I don't wish to overwork you.

Dad said I wasn't to play my guitar — but I can work on this song I'm composing.

Next day at school, Rama played the composition to Miss Ainsley, the music and drama teacher.

♫ You only care when you want to — ♪ And you'll break my heart before long.

The music and words go beautifully together, Rama. You have a real gift for music.

I'm willing to give you extra lessons during lunch breaks and after school if you like. No charge of course!

That would be great, but —

Sometimes my father likes me to help out in the restaurant. Not many hours — just to learn a little about it.

Just during the odd lunch hour, then.

On Saturday evening, Rama was helping her father.

You have a real flair for dressing the table, Rama.

I like to see it looking nice for the customers.

Hello, Mr Chand. A table for three, please?

Certainly, Mr Peters.

I wish I could arrange flowers like that, Rama. I only have to look at them and they wither!

What it is to be talented! Miss Ainsley's always saying how good Rama is, when she has extra music lessons during the lunch hour, Mr Chand!

Oh, really?

A word please, Rama.

So, extra lessons, eh? I don't mind you playing and singing for fun — but you dedicate too much time to music, Rama!

But I want to be a singer and musician when I leave school.

That evening, Rama had come to her decision, and slipped out to the telephone box —

There! I've said I *WILL* take part in the musical. Surely if we won, and Edwin Green gave me and my songs good marks, Dad would realise how much my music means to me?

Working a few hours in the restaurant was normally no problem, but preparing for the musical as well was hard work. However, Rama was determined to see it through.

Yawn! I must get the words of this last song learned by tomorrow.

If I do the dance steps too, it will help to fix them in my mind.

Suddenly, there was a knock at the door —

Rama? Are you all right? I heard some bumping noises?

Er — yes, Dad.

I've heard you pacing about and talking to yourself a lot lately. Is anything wrong?

No, Dad. Just a school — er — project. Nothing to worry about, really.

It sounds like too much. Shall I have a word with your headmaster?

Oh, no — no thanks. I'll have finished it by next week.

That was no lie, the musical will be over on Saturday. Dad has agreed to let me go to the school festival — but I daren't tell him I'm actually taking part. I know he'd forbid it.

I don't like deceiving him — but singing and playing my guitar is all I really want to do.

During the week's run-up to the festival, Rama found it increasingly difficult to concentrate on anything but the musical.

We are the ones who will change the world, ♪ ♫ We are the ones who give you our word—

Rama! The sauce will burn!

Oh, sorry. It's all right.

You're looking tired. A couple of early nights, tonight and tomorrow, eh?

I'm fine, really! And I'm looking forward to the festival tomorrow night!

Oh, very well. I guess I'm being over-protective!

Next day, Rama found it hard to conceal her excitement —

Don't put me down, Cos I'm happy!

Ha-ha! That makes two of us, Rama. I've some exciting news!

I've been reliably informed that Ronald Egon, the famous food critic, will eat here tonight. If he mentions us favourably in his next guide book, we'll be made!

He's very keen on family-run businesses, so naturally, I will need you to waitress.

But I can't — the festival!

Oh, you can go to another one some time. It's not as though you *HAVE* to be there. No, you *MUST* be here. Now I'll tell Som.

What shall I do? I can't tell Dad I'm the lead singer in the musical, and I dread to think how angry he would be if I went to the festival. He'd never forgive me.

But if I don't go, I'll be letting Miss Ainsley and the cast down — and I'll miss my chance of being 'discovered' by Edwin Green. Oh, what should I do?

CONTINUED ON PAGE 113

80

CHESTER'S STORY

IN THE BAG

HI there — I'm Chester the chimp, and I live in a zoo. To be quite honest, I'd rather be larking about in the jungle with my cousins. But if all us animals took off back where we came from, you lot wouldn't have anything to come and gape at — and zoos would go out of business. Besides, there wouldn't be interesting things like ladies' handbags in the jungle. That's what I want to tell you about — the day someone nicked a lady's handbag in our zoo. Well, it was little me, actually —

*   *   *   *

I've always been fascinated by handbags. Most of the females who visit the zoo, arrive clutching them. They come in all shapes and sizes — the handbags I mean — though their owners are all shapes and sizes, too. Some are shiny black leather bags, which you could almost see your face in. Mind you, I never want to see *MY* face in anything! Some are a horrible brown shade, like Bertie the brown bear, when he's having an off-day. Some are grey and bulging in odd places, like Hannah Hippo. And one lady told her friend that *HER* handbag was made of real snake-skin! Of course, I rushed to the corner nearest the reptile house, and

shouted to warn Percy Python that he might end up as a handbag. Rotten of me, wasn't it? Poor Percy was probably "snaking" with fright!

Anyway, whatever the handbags looked like, I was desperate to know what was in them all. And one visiting-hour, when I was going for a stroll with Mr Zebedee, the zoo-keeper, I almost found out. A lady opened her handbag right beside me, and I peered in, my heart thumping with excitement. But before I could glimpse the contents, Mr Zebedee dragged me off!

"Mind your own business, Chester," he laughed. So that was *THAT!*

But then another day, the zoo-keeper gave my sister, Charlotte, a handbag. Well, Charlotte has always had airs and graces — or should I say, *HAIRS* and graces — but there was no stopping her, after she got the handbag! She minced around with it, on one hairy arm, as if she was the original Queen of the Jungle. I was beside myself with curiosity.

"Please, Charlotte — let me see what's in it," I begged.

"Get lost!" said Charlotte rudely. And after me asking her so politely! But I was determined to find out what was in her handbag. So I waited until Charlotte lay

down for her afternoon beauty sleep — or *UGLY* sleep, in her case — then I crept up and slid the handbag off her hairy arm.

One gentle *CLICK* of the clasp, and I had it open. But there wasn't a thing in it — no kidding!

"What a let-down," I muttered to myself. "And fancy Charlotte carrying around an *EMPTY* handbag! She's doing it for show, all right!"

But as I slid the handbag back on to Charlotte's arm, she went and woke up. Well, she promptly went *BANANAS!* And do you know what she did? She hit me on the head with her handbag! Ouch! I had a lump on my nut for days after, and I wished I'd never touched her wretched bag.

But I was still keen to see inside *OTHER* handbags. And, the very next visiting hour, I was out for yet another stroll, with Mr Zebedee, when a very nice-looking lady passed us, with her daughter. Well, I guessed it was her daughter, because they looked

so like each other. Charlotte and our Mum look like each other, too — both dead ugly! But, to get back to the story —

The lady and her daughter stopped beside Emily Elephant's pen.

"Let's take a photo of that pretty elephant," the little girl said to her Mum. "PRETTY? She must be needing glasses," I thought. Pretty *AWFUL* would be more like it. Emily was so fat, I was sure they would need six pictures end to end, to get her all in.

But the next minute, I forgot all about Emily — because the lady put her smart red handbag down on a bench! It was all mine for the grabbing — so I yanked my hairy hand out of Mr Zebedee's, snatched up the bag, and took off with it to a quiet spot behind the reptile house!

I was trembling from top to toe with excitement as I opened the clasp of the bag. At last I was going to see what was inside. I tipped the bag upside down, and everything tumbled out on the ground. I stared down eagerly —

There was a comb — I recognised that because the zoo-keeper uses one on me, to get rid of fleas. Humans must have fleas, too, I thought — fancy that! And there was a bag of sweets.

"Yummy," I thought, helping myself. "The lady won't miss one or two —"

There were some soft, white papery things, too. I don't know what you call them, but I've seen humans putting them to their noses and making snuffly noises — but the rest of the things were a bit of a mystery. Two funny little books, and a set of silvery things that jangled on a ring — and a man's face in a sort of frame thing. It wasn't wrinkled old Mr Zebedee. The man was better-looking than HIM!

I was just on my sixth sweet, when Mr Zebedee and the lady's

daughter came tearing round the corner of the reptile house, looking for me.

"So there you are! You're for it," screeched Mr Zebedee. He was snorting like an angry rhino as he grabbed me.

"Please, don't be too hard on him," begged the girl as she shoved her Mum's things back in the handbag. But Mr Zebedee was hard on me, all right. You'd think I had committed the great train robbery, the way HE went on. He dragged me back to our enclosure, and told me that I would get no treats for the next two days! That meant no chocolate, no peanut bars, no ice-cream, NOTHING!

"Life won't be worth living," I gulped, feeling sorry for myself. "Can I share YOUR treats, Charlotte?"

"Not likely!" said Charlotte, snootily. "YOU stole the handbag, so you must suffer the consequences, Chester!"

I might have known not to expect any sympathy from HER!

But a week later, a box with a gi-normous bit of chocolate cake was delivered to the zoo — for yours truly! I couldn't believe my luck. There was a letter with it, and that was for me, too. Mr Zebedee read it out to me, as I tore into the choccy cake, and this is what it said —

Dear Chester,

Thank you for snatching my Mum's handbag last week, and emptying it out. You see, some weeks ago, my Mum and Dad had a terrible row. Mum told Dad to get lost, and that's just what he did. He packed his things, and went to stay

with my Gran, and Mum said she never wanted to see him again. I knew Dad was sorry, and wanted to make things up, because he kept phoning — but Mum wouldn't speak to him, not even on the phone. Mum said that she and Dad were finished, and I believed her — until YOU upturned her handbag. You see, one of the things that fell out was her favourite photo of Dad, in a frame — so I realised she STILL cared for him, deep down. I rang Dad from a phone-box in the zoo — and when we got home, Dad was waiting with a big bouquet of flowers for Mum. Everything's all right now — and it's thanks to YOU, Chester. This is a bit of Dad's favourite cake that Mum's just made for him. Hope you enjoy it.

Love, Amy.

*   *   *   *

I wasn't too sure what THAT was all about. I scratched my head — and every other bit of me, while I was at it — but I couldn't make head nor tail of it, for PEANUTS! If you ask me, humans do pretty daft things at times. Their lives get so complicated, not like us simple animals. Still, there must be something in this handbag-snatching, because it got me this yummy chocolate cake. So maybe I'll have another go at it some day soon!

P.S. If you want to know if I gave Charlotte any cake, the answer's NO!

THE END

83

Next morning—

I thought I'd come for you, Jenny. Hey — you're not even dressed! Did you forget about the match?

What match, Laura? It's off, isn't it? Kim rang last night to say it was cancelled, so Mum's gone shopping and I was having a lie-in. Did nobody phone *YOU*?

No, because the match is definitely *ON!* I've just seen three other girls in our team going down to the sports field. But you'll still make it if you rush, Jenny. I'll make some toast for you, while you dress!

Thanks, Laura — I'm dead annoyed about this!

Kim must have been trying to stop me turning up, so *SHE'D* be asked to stand in! I never thought she could stoop so low!

Nor me — but it just shows you, doesn't it? Still, I'd rather you didn't make a big thing of it.

We'll just make it in time, so please don't mention this to Miss Hardie. I don't want Kim dropped from the team altogether, even though she *DID* try a mean trick on you!

You're a good friend to her, Laura. She doesn't deserve you! Okay — I won't tell Miss Hardie — but I *WILL* let Kim know what I think of her!

Jenny's chance came at half-time—

You little sneak, Kim Fox — that was a disgusting trick to play, phoning to say the match was off. Thought you'd get a game, didn't you? But luckily Laura came for me, so your nasty scheme fell flat on its face.

What are you on about? I didn't phone you, Jenny!

Yes, you did. My Mum took the message, and she never makes mistakes with names — so stop trying to cover up!

I'm not trying to cover up anything. I *DIDN'T* phone you, and that's the honest truth.

YOU made that phone call, pretending to be me — didn't you, Laura Rice?

Maybe I did — maybe I didn't! But one thing's certain, Jenny won't go to your party after this, and she'll no doubt put some of her mates off going, as well. Which means more guests for ME!

But, two days later, at lunchtime—

I'm still trying to think of a way to get my own back on Laura, and make HER lose some party guests! She's just won two pounds on the fruit machine.

And later, at break—

I'm collecting fifty pence from everyone, to buy something for Lesley Moore in hospital.

Right, Claire — here's my fifty pence. I'll help you get the rest, if you like.

And so—

Much as I don't like having to speak to you, I'm collecting for Lesley's present — so fifty pence, please.

I'll give you seventy pence — I can afford it after winning two pounds on the fruit machine.

Later—

Thanks, Kim. Did everyone fork out willingly?

Everyone except Laura Rice. She only gave me twenty pence, and it took me all my time to get even THAT out of her!

But she'd just had a win on the fruit machine! How mean can you get?

That's what I thought, too. I didn't know Laura was so tight-fisted!

87

After school, as Kim and Laura ignored each other at a bus stop—

BUS STOP

Maybe see you tonight, Kim!

Sure, Scott!

He's a cert for *MY* party — especially if we get on well tonight!

Don't be so sure!

Kim's gone to sit at the front of the bus with someone else — so I'll stay at the door. I don't want to go anywhere near *HER!*

Then, some streets later—

There's Scott's gran getting off — she lives at his home.

Oh, no! She's tripped!

I'll help her!

Thanks, love — I can't keep the other passengers waiting.

Tomorrow, Kim — didn't she tell you? I expect *YOU'LL* be the first to get one.

Laura obviously hasn't told her Mum about the two parties. I didn't tell my parents, either — they're fond of Laura, and they'd be upset by all this. At the last minute I'll say she's ill and can't come.

But I'm glad I've found out when Laura's giving out her invites. I'll beat her to it, by going round with mine *TONIGHT!*

But, that evening—

You can't go out in that, Kim — it's lashing. You can hand out the invitations at school tomorrow.

I suppose I'll have to. But I can still put mine out before Laura, if I get to school before her.

So, next morning—

There's Laura rushing for the bus — but I won't ask the conductor to hold it for her.

But—

I saw you just miss the bus, Laura. Do you want a lift?

Yes please, Mrs Arthur!

90

And, when Kim arrived at school—

Laura's here, and handing out her invites! How did she manage it?

Mrs Arthur, the new French teacher, gave me a lift. It serves you right for not holding the bus for me! I've got half my invites given out already.

So what? It doesn't matter who gets them out first. It's who's the most popular that counts.

But their friends weren't too happy.

What's going on? We can't come to two parties, on the same day!

I know — so you have to choose, Sally!

Hers — or mine!

But, two days before the parties—

This is awful — not one person has said they're coming to MY party, so they must all be going to Laura's. They must prefer her to me, and it really hurts!

And, that night—

The party's off, because Laura's having one, too — and everyone's going to hers!

Oh, that's a shame, love. It's just as well I haven't done any baking yet.

We'll take you out for a meal at the Cafe Royale instead!

Thanks, Dad!

But a party was what I *REALLY* wanted! Everyone will have a great time at Laura's party, and I won't even be asked to that, now we've fallen out. I'm the loser, all right!

On Saturday night—

Time to leave, Kim.

I haven't the heart for a meal out, but I can't let Mum and Dad down.

We'll be passing Laura's house any minute, but I won't look. I can't bear to see all her guests arriving.

But, to Kim's surprise—

Look, love — Laura's house is in darkness — there's no sign of a party.

That's odd!

92

At the Café Royale—

The reception room is at the back—

Reception room? I thought that was just for weddings and such like.

To Kim's amazement—

Happy birthday, Kim.

Laura — and her Mum and Dad — and all our friends!

I'm afraid we just couldn't choose between your two parties — and anyway, we wanted to help you to make up.

So we got together with both sets of parents, and they booked this place for a big joint party.

I — I can't believe it! I thought everyone was going to YOUR party, Laura!

And I thought everyone must be going to YOURS! Our fantastic friends and parents have more sense than us, Kim! We were idiots to fall out.

So we were — let's be friends again.

And that made the thirteenth birthday party REALLY special!

KIM AND LAURA V3

13

ATTRACTIVE ANGIE

A STRANGE cosmetic lotion had made Angie Adams very attractive — in a MAGNETIC sort of way!

I missed the bus! I'm late for the charity fete!

At the fete —

Mum sent these meat pies for your bakery stall, Mrs Brown.

That's kind of her, Angie.

Suddenly, a pie leaped up at Angie! She ducked, and —

URRGH!

Oh, no! Mrs Snodgrass!

Who threw that pie at me?

I certainly didn't!

Er — neither did I.

Well, not purposely!

When I get hot and bothered, my magnetism starts to work overtime — and Mum baked those pies in metal foil cases! I'd better get away from here, before I set the lot flying around!

x

94

YE OLD MAGIC WISHING WELL

Throw in a coin and have your wish granted!

It's just another fete gimmick, of course, but —

— I wish it could make me less attractive!

Help! My magnetism seems to attract COINS too!

AHA! Caught you! First you throw pies — now you steal coins from the wishing pool!

No — I was just picking them up, Mrs Snodgrass.

Put them back! I shall report this to your mother!

It's no use trying to explain.

A little later —

Crumbs, that antique stall is full of metal stuff. I'd better not go near it, while I still feel so bothered.

I'M Sally Jardine, and, not so long ago, I belonged to a VERY close family. Well, with Mum, Dad, me, Pam, Donna, Joe, Tickles the cat and Butch the dog — all crammed together in a two-bedroomed council flat, we couldn't be anything ELSE but close! Talk about sardines in a tin — we were the JARDINES in a tin!

We definitely needed a bigger house. But trying to get one from our local council was as hard as extracting wisdom teeth from a bad-tempered crocodile! Oh, yes — we were supposedly quite high up on that elusive thing they call the 'waiting list'! But HOW high up, was anybody's guess. Mum and Dad were forever trekking down to the housing office, to try to find out.

One day, out of sheer desperation, they took us lot with them. We all straggled in, Mum, Dad, me, Pam, Donna, Joe, Tickles and Butch — and sat in a heart-rending row, until Dad was called to face the lady on the other side of the grid.

"We really DO need a bigger house, as you can see," pleaded Dad, waving a hand in our direction. "There are EIGHT of us!"

"Animals don't count," she said. "And I am afraid you are not the ONLY ones on our waiting list, Mr Jardine. So you will just have to take your turn!"

We all straggled out again, fed-up.

"Why can't the council employ fairy godmothers, who could grant us a bigger house, or even an extra bedroom on the one we've got, with a flick of their council-supplied ballpoints?" I thought miserably.

Jardines In A Tin!
SALLY'S STORY

"I wish we could afford to BUY a house," moaned Mum.

"I know — but we CAN'T, so we'll just have to wait, like she says," sighed Dad.

How I detested that word, WAIT. It meant more days, and more nights, sharing a poky bedroom with my younger sisters, Pam and Donna. I slept in a single bed, while they had bunk beds, and privacy was a word I knew nothing about. I'd long since given up keeping a diary, because I'd run out of places to hide it from their prying eyes. And I didn't ask my friends round any more. I used to feel bad because I was always at THEIR houses — so once or twice in the past, I have invited them to mine, but it was never a success. One particular night finished things for me.

"I've asked Hannah and Jill round, so I want you two to keep out of the bedroom," I told Pam and Donna.

"What's it worth?" asked scheming Pam, sticking her greedy paw out.

"Yeah — how much?" enquired Donna, following suit. So I was obliged to give them fifty pence each, before they made their exit. What a pity I'd chosen the night there was a big football match on the box. You know, the match no Dad, or brother, can miss! And, just as I'd settled down with my mates for a good gossip, the bedroom door opened, and Mum shoved Pam and Donna back in, her face apologetic.

"Sorry, love," she sighed. "But they can't do their homework in the living-room, with that racket on the telly. They'll have to do it in here."

"Yeah — and we can't do it, if people are TALKING," said Pam, smugly.

"We'd better go then," said Jill and Hannah, getting to their feet.

I was furious.

"Money back then," I snarled, when I'd seen them off. But, would you believe it — those two twisters had been and gone and spent it, on sweets. So I'd lost out all round. After that, I gave up entertaining as a lost cause!

* * * *

Then there was the night before my important maths test.

Nights weren't much of an improvement on days, in our bedroom. Donna snored like a demented rhino, and Pam babbled rubbish in her sleep.

"You two had better be quiet tonight," I warned them. "I want a decent night's sleep, before my test."

"I don't know I'm going to snore, do I?" sniffed Donna, not unreasonably. But I wasn't in the mood for being reasonable.

"Maybe not — but just make sure you DON'T!" I snapped.

"Do you mind if we BREATHE?" asked Pam, sarkily.

"No, but make sure that's all," I muttered.

But, ten minutes into their dreamland, the racket started.

Donna started her pig imitations, with a vengeance. So I got out of bed, and heaved her over on to her side. That was difficult, as she sleeps on the top bunk, and is built like a tank. But no sooner had I crawled back into my own downie, when she flopped on to her back again, and gave it big licks. I could swear she was doing it out of spite!

Then Pam started to spout garbage, from the bunk below. She made even LESS sense than she did during the day. No kidding — it was like trying to sleep in the zoo!

I felt like a zombie, next day, as I blundered through my maths test — and I blamed it on THEM!

"You look fed-up," remarked Tina Laing, in the playground, afterwards. Tina wasn't my best friend, but I got on well with her.

"Yeah — well, I won't be surprised if I get MINUS something, in that test," I moaned. "I got hardly any sleep last night, thanks to my sisters!"

"That's a shame," sympathised Tina. "Listen — if you're not doing anything else, what about coming round to MY house tonight? We could play some tapes."

"Brill," I sighed. Anything to get away from the two monsters I had to share a room with. And, that evening, I escaped round to Tina's smart bungalow. It was the first time I'd been there, and I was soon drooling with envy. Tina was an only child, and she had a fantastic bedroom of her own. Everything a girl could ever want was in it

—luxury fitments, her own telly — she even had a dead trendy *PHONE* at her bedside.

"This is heaven on earth," I thought silently, as I sank my feet into the sheepskin rugs on her bedroom floor. Why did Tina have so much, when *I* had so little? Why was life so unfair?

Back in our own, over-crowded flat, I couldn't help feeling resentful. "Tina has it all," I thought. "And I have nothing — just a third of a poky bedroom! If only I could swop places with her!"

But I was to be even *MORE* envious, yet. A couple of weeks later, some of us were arranging to go to the pictures, on Saturday night.

"You coming?" I asked Tina. But she shook her head, smilingly.

"Sorry," she said. "But I'm going to Shingleford for the weekend. We've bought a holiday flat there — so we'll be going most weekends, and holidays!"

I couldn't believe what I was hearing. Shingleford was a seaside resort, some miles up the coast. Now Tina had *TWO* homes, while I only had one over-crowded one! I was well and truly filled with envy!

Then, just before the summer hols, Dad and Mum told us they'd booked a caravan at Shingleford, for us lot, for two weeks! So I told Tina I'd be able to visit her, at her holiday home.

"You don't have to bother, Sally," she said. "I mean, we're not really *NEAR* the caravan site!"

"That doesn't matter — Dad can bring me, in our car," I smiled. It occurred to me that Tina didn't seem too keen on my visiting her at Shingleford. Maybe she'd already made friends there, I mused. Still, I wouldn't interfere, if she had.

Needless to say, the caravan at Shingleford wasn't big enough for us, either! In fact, there was even *LESS* room for the eight of us, than in our two-bedroomed house back home.

"If there's ever a competition for squashing as many people into a phone box as possible, us Jardines would win," I thought, grimly, as we fought for beds. Almost everything, except the tiny caravan sink, converted into a bed — and I had the misfortune to land with the bed that was the one and only table, by day. So my holiday lie-ins went out of the window. I was turfed out of bed every morning, so the rest of them could get the table down, for breakfast.

Mind you, it wasn't too bad when the sun shone, because then we all got outside. But when it rained, we were cooped up like bad-tempered chickens, and one wet day, I'd had enough! So I asked Dad to drive me over to Tina's holiday flat.

When we tracked it down, it was a smart, Victorian flat with new, double-glazed windows, at the posh residential end of Shingleford.

"I'll pick you up later," grinned Dad, as he rattled

off in our banger, leaving me to tap timidly at the impressive brass door-knocker.

"Oh. Er — hi, Sally — come in," smiled Tina. But again, I sensed she wasn't too happy to see me. Inside, it was a beautiful flat, and Tina's bedroom was just as gorgeous as the other one. Tina's Dad was reading, in the spacious lounge. He looked up and smiled, but there was an emptiness about his smile I couldn't quite put my finger on.

"Maybe Tina will fix you something to eat," he said.

So we went into the fitted kitchen, the sort you see in magazines.

"Has your Mum gone shopping?" I asked, conversationally. But the answer I got took me totally by surprise.

"No, she hasn't," muttered Tina. "I might as well tell you, Sally. This is Dad's flat, not Mum's. She doesn't live here. The truth is, I don't have a happy home like *YOU*, any more. I have to shunt between Mum and Dad. But I was too embarrassed to tell anyone before — so I pretended I had a second, *HOLIDAY* home."

So *THAT* was why Tina hadn't wanted me to visit her.

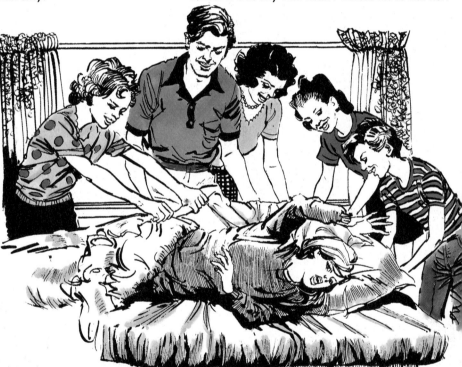

She didn't want me to know the truth. But now I *DID*, I found myself feeling really sorry for her.

"Well, it's better for them to be apart, if they don't get on — and better for you, too," I said, trying to cheer her up.

"I suppose so," sighed Tina, but her face was bleak. "But how lucky you are, having all your family together!"

I had a lot to think about, as we took turns to breathe, back in our cramped caravan. Even though we *WERE* over-crowded, I realised who really *WAS* the lucky one — *ME!*

P.S. Soon after we returned from Shingleford, our name reached the top of the waiting list, at last — and we're now in a comfortable four-bedroomed semi.

But Tina's still got her two homes.

THE END

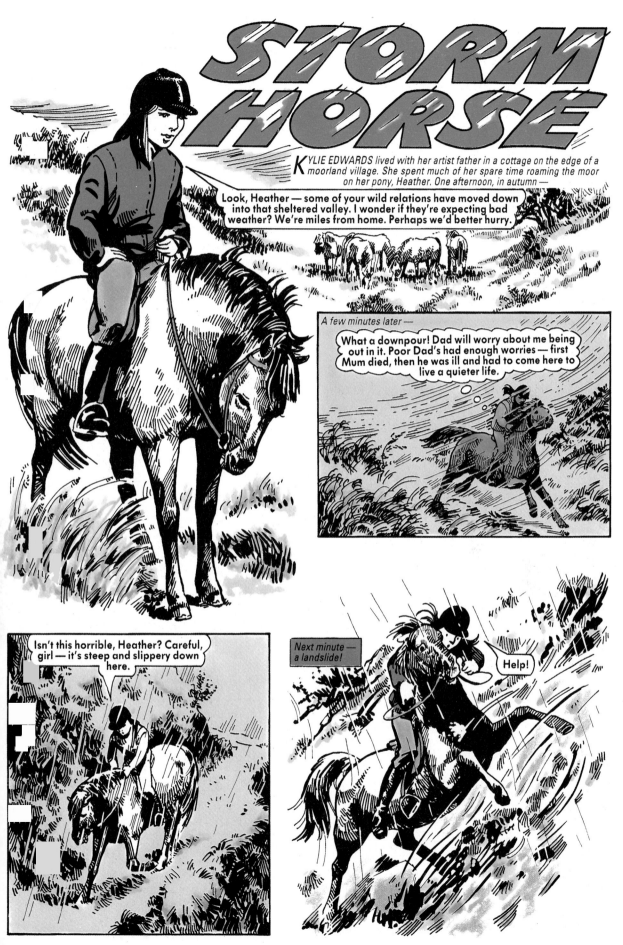

STORM HORSE

KYLIE EDWARDS lived with her artist father in a cottage on the edge of a moorland village. She spent much of her spare time roaming the moor on her pony, Heather. One afternoon, in autumn —

Look, Heather — some of your wild relations have moved down into that sheltered valley. I wonder if they're expecting bad weather? We're miles from home. Perhaps we'd better hurry.

A few minutes later —

What a downpour! Dad will worry about me being out in it. Poor Dad's had enough worries — first Mum died, then he was ill and had to come here to live a quieter life.

Isn't this horrible, Heather? Careful, girl — it's steep and slippery down here.

Next minute — a landslide!

Help!

It's all right, Heather. Even if we have to stay here all night, someone will find us in the end.

That bush broke our fall, thank goodness. But how do we get back on to the path?

Steady, Heather — I'm trying to find a way up.

But as soon as I try to step beyond this ledge, my feet slip — and it's getting so dark that I can't see any possible way to go.

As soon as Heather saw the horse, she headed towards it.

Then —

It's a horse! How did he get over there? It's a sheer drop from above.

Heather — stop! You'll slip!

But the mystery horse led them on a pathway that he seemed to know.

Slowly, Heather — good girl.

That horse — he — he doesn't look REAL!

He-he's gone! Maybe he wasn't really there at all.

It was an eerie thought —

Almost home, Heather — thanks to that grey horse. Thinking about him now is a bit creepy — but real or not, he did help us.

Ten minutes later —

I was worried, Kylie. You're so late, and the storm is pretty fierce.

We're fine, Dad. The path got washed away a bit, but we were all right.

I won't tell Dad about our fall, or the grey horse. He'd only worry, and he might try to stop me going off on my own with Heather. I'd hate that.

But Kylie couldn't stop thinking about the grey horse —

He must have been real — just a big moor pony, maybe, who had slipped down the hill like Heather did. Yet he looked much bigger than a pony, and he seemed so sure-footed. And there are no such things as ghosts, or magical horses. I must try to find out more about him.

Two days later, it was Kylie's half-term holiday —

So we're both off for a day in the hills, Kylie — you on a long ride, me to do a bit of painting at Low Lake. But be back before dark — the moor is treacherous at night, even if you do know it well.

I will, Dad.

101

Later —

There's a herd of moor ponies, but there isn't a grey. Could I possibly have imagined the whole thing?

And then —

There he is! We DIDN'T imagine him, Heather! Let's try to get closer.

He's a horse, not a moor pony — he looks like an Arabian.

He isn't going to let me get near him!

There he goes. But if he ISN'T magic, he MUST have come from somewhere. I'm going to try following him.

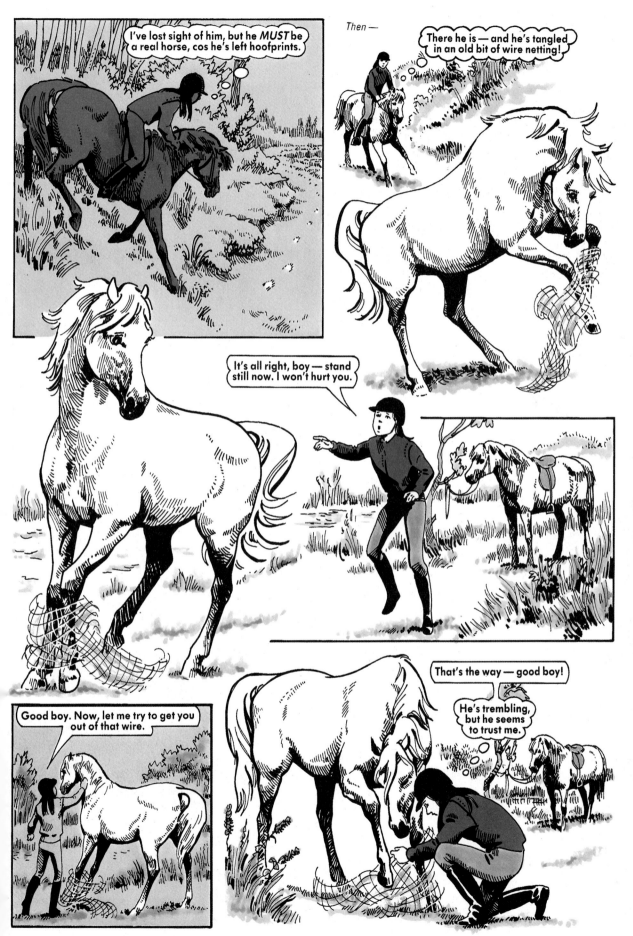

There, you're free now, and you aren't hurt.

Who can he belong to? And how can I lead him home? I've nothing to put on his head.

Come on, boy.

Perhaps he'll follow Heather. A horse like him shouldn't be running loose on the moor.

Go on, Heather — he's coming.

If he'll follow me home, I can get him into the paddock and telephone the police. SOMEONE must be looking for him.

A little later —

Hello, Mr Morris. Listen, this grey horse that's following me — do you know who owns him?

Grey horse, Kylie — where?

Are you having me on, lass? I can't see a grey horse.

He's gone — but he really was there, I promise you! He was an Arabian and he followed us from Deep Coombe.

And now he's vanished, just like he did before.

When old Isaac Croft died, way over at High Healey, his whole stud was sold off at auction. He had Arabs — perhaps one got loose, and wasn't missed.

He must have galloped off when he saw Mr Morris.

104

Later, back home —

He was the most beautiful horse I've ever seen. You liked him, too — didn't you, Heather? I wonder if we'll ever see him again.

That night

I heard a horse whinnying — and it DIDN'T sound like Heather!

The grey — he's here!

If I can catch him, I'll shut him in Heather's stable for the night. Then tomorrow I can look for his owner.

Come on, boy — look, I've got some oats for you.

He doesn't seem real in the moonlight — he looks truly magical!

Great! He's let me put on the head-collar. Now to get him into the stable.

I'll get you some hay, and Heather will be out here to keep you company.

He doesn't like being shut in much — or wearing a head collar. I'll take it off again, before leaving him for the night.

A little later —

I hope I can find his owner, and that it's someone who will look after him well.

Next morning —

It's turned really wet and stormy again. I can't see the grey — he must be sheltering well back inside the stable.

I'll come and take a look at the horse, Kylie. I remember reading about the High Healey auction. The old man was deep in debt, and everything had to go.

Then perhaps the grey got away before he was sold, so no one missed him? You'll like him, Dad — he'd make a lovely model for a painting.

But when they reached the stable —

He's gone! But I shut the door, and it's STILL shut!

Sure you weren't dreaming, love? A wild, grey Arabian horse, jumping into our paddock, does sound a bit dreamlike.

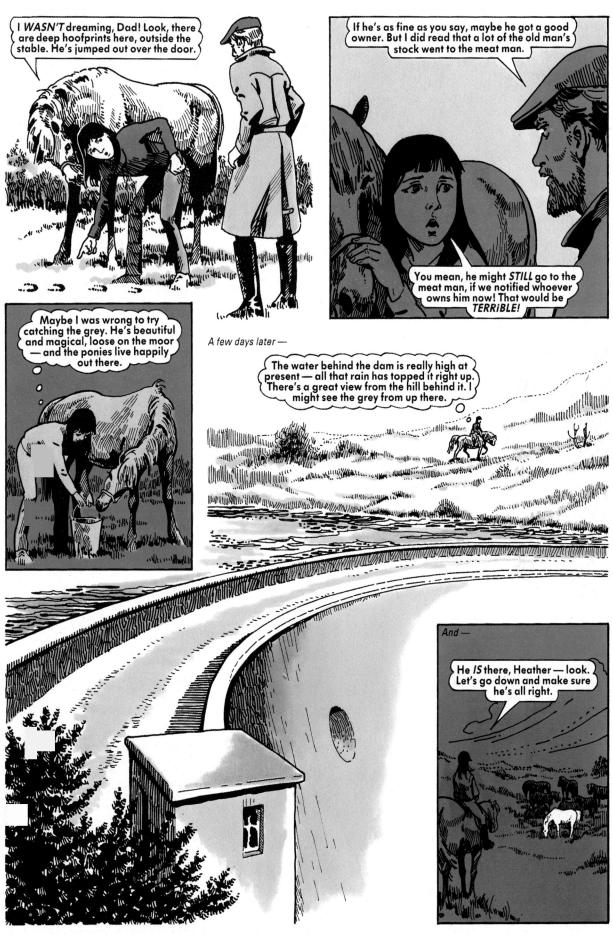

I *WASN'T* dreaming, Dad! Look, there are deep hoofprints here, outside the stable. He's jumped out over the door.

If he's as fine as you say, maybe he got a good owner. But I did read that a lot of the old man's stock went to the meat man.

You mean, he might *STILL* go to the meat man, if we notified whoever owns him now! That would be *TERRIBLE!*

Maybe I was wrong to try catching the grey. He's beautiful and magical, loose on the moor — and the ponies live happily out there.

A few days later —

The water behind the dam is really high at present — all that rain has topped it right up. There's a great view from the hill behind it. I might see the grey from up there.

And —

He *IS* there, Heather — look. Let's go down and make sure he's all right.

107

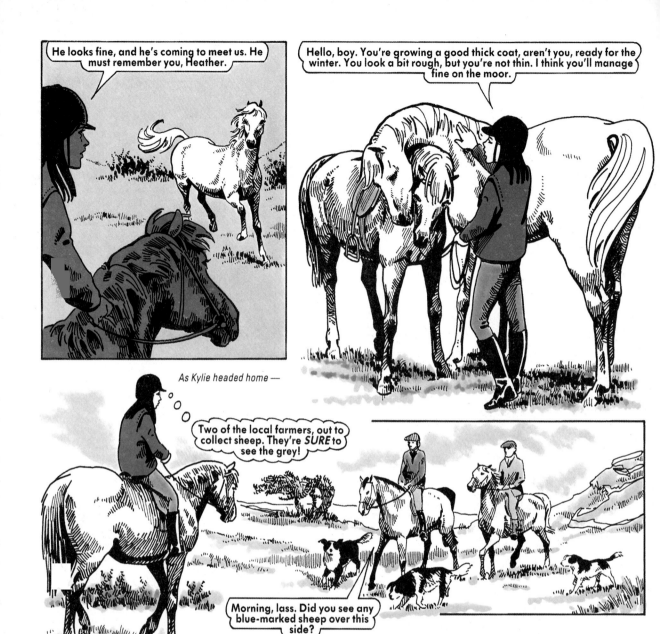

He looks fine, and he's coming to meet us. He must remember you, Heather.

Hello, boy. You're growing a good thick coat, aren't you, ready for the winter. You look a bit rough, but you're not thin. I think you'll manage fine on the moor.

As Kylie headed home —

Two of the local farmers, out to collect sheep. They're *SURE* to see the grey!

Morning, lass. Did you see any blue-marked sheep over this side?

Er — no, sorry.

The grey — he's vanished again!

He seems to trust *ME*, but runs when he hears or senses strangers. And yet — sometimes I still feel it's only me who *SEES* him!

Two nights later —

It's the grey — and he looks upset! I'd better go down.

He's off — almost as if he wants me to follow him. I'll grab Heather's bridle, and my old hat, from the stable.

Soon —

He's heading for the dam, and the place I last saw him. I wonder if there's anything wrong with the moor ponies?

But to Kylie's horror —

The dam is leaking! I must warn the village — and get the dam sluices opened!

Go on, Heather — faster!

Soon —

See, lass — they're on their way up to the dam. Looks as if they'll be in time — and if they're not, at least we're all safe, thanks to you.

And the grey, Dad — *HE* warned me!

Next day —

The dam's safe — but where is the grey, I wonder? Will I see him again, or was he just a dream?

But, a few months later —

Heather — what a surprise!

I thought she was getting a bit fat, and slow. I never dreamed she could be in foal.

Your foal has an Arabian head, Heather. So he *WAS* real, my magical storm horse — and this is the proof. We'll call the foal Storm — because that's where his father came from, out of the storm. He may have been half magic, but your baby is *REAL* — so neither of us will ever forget my Storm Horse.

110

THE END

JOINING ST JOHN'S

ABOUT a year ago, Mum was given two tickets for "The Yeomen of the Guard". None of her friends could go with her so she said, "Come with me, Katy. I don't like going on my own, and your Dad won't come."

I grumbled a bit. Well, the show sounded a bit fuddy-duddy to me — but Mum's a good sort, she'd do anything for anybody, so I said I'd go.

Do you know, it was brilliant! I really fell for old Gilbert and Sullivan. Mum was pleased, too, because I had enjoyed it.

I started buying the records after that. My brothers, who are older than me, teased me no end. They'd start singing "I'm Called Little Buttercup, Dear Little Buttercup" — or "Take A Pair Of Sparkling Eyes", if I was excited about something.

Then one day I heard that "The Pirates of Penzance" would be on at our local theatre for one night only. It was Mum's WI night, so she couldn't come, but Dad said he would take me down. I hadn't much money, but Pete and Jim — they're my two brothers — gave me £1 each, Mum gave me some and Dad made it up. He said it was my pocket-money in advance but I could hear Mum laughing in the kitchen when he said it. I'm the only girl so I get spoilt a bit.

"The Pirates of Penzance" was just as good as I had hoped.

For the first time, I noticed the St John Ambulance girls standing at the back. They weren't much older than me, and suddenly I had an idea. If I joined, I could come to the theatre free! I thought about it during the interval and glanced back at them every now and then. The uniform was okay, and they looked as if they were having a great time.

My Dad came to pick me up in the car. He had picked Mum up from her WI meeting and she was sitting in the front.

"Did you enjoy it?" they both asked.

"It was great — really great," I said.

After a few moments, I saw them glancing at each other.

"You're sure you enjoyed it?" Mum said.

Of course, they had noticed that I wasn't spouting away like I usually do, so I told them straight what was on my mind.

"I'm going to join the junior branch of the St John Ambulance Association."

"Good grief!" Dad said, avoiding a cyclist by inches.

"But you don't like blood and — er — things," Mum said.

"No," I spoke eagerly now. "But I'll be able to go to the theatre free. I could go to all sorts of different things, football matches and — "

"You'll have to learn a lot first," Dad broke in. "It's no good going to a football match if you can't revive anybody." He chuckled to himself and I knew he was thinking of me trying to revive a twelve-stone footballer.

"I *shall* join!" I said. "You don't mind, do you, Mum?"

"No. I think it's a good idea," she said.

KATY'S STORY

So I joined. It was hard work, but I got stuck into it and I passed two exams quite quickly.

After that, they let me go to the local hospital on Sundays and take some of the patients in wheelchairs over to the chapel for hymn-singing. You'd never believe how difficult it is to wheel a heavy man through a ward with one leg bandaged. I was dead scared that I'd knock his leg against one of the beds.

Then one Sunday morning I had to take an old lady along to the chapel. I was sure she had been crying.

"Have you got a pain anywhere, Mrs Thomas?" I asked.

"No, dear," she said. "I'm getting better now."

Then why was she crying, I asked myself?

"When are you going home?"

"I don't know." Her voice quivered and I knew she really *was* crying.

One thing I learned from the St John's classes was that if a person was worrying about something she didn't get well so quickly, so I stopped the wheelchair, went round and looked into Mrs Thomas's face. Her eyes were full of tears and she was holding a handkerchief up to her nose.

"What's wrong, Mrs Thomas?" I asked.

"It's my cat!" Mrs Thomas gulped.

Then I got the whole story out of her.

"The boy next door — Paul, his name is — said he would look after him, but he doesn't really understand animals," she said. "You see, I was rushed into hospital and didn't have time to arrange anything." She sniffed. "It was raining this morning and I wondered where he was. He's never out in the rain and he's quite old."

"I'll find out for you, Mrs Thomas," I said. "Don't worry any more. I'll go along there this afternoon."

Well, I couldn't let the poor old thing worry like that, could I?

Mum was great when I got home. She felt sorry for Mrs Thomas.

"Get out of that uniform," she said. "And you can borrow my bike."

She cut a big slice off the roast chicken and chopped it up.

"There. Give the cat that," she said.

It didn't seem far on Mum's bike and I soon found the house. There was a young chap next door, messing about with an old car. That must be Paul, I thought. He looked up when I went in the gateway, so I said,

"I've come to see Mrs Thomas's cat," which sounded a bit thin, I thought.

He didn't seem to think it odd, though, and said, "It's over by the shed."

It was a nice cat, a fat tabby. I got out the chicken pieces and put them on the concrete path for him. I looked in the shed. It was clean and there was a cat bed in the corner.

"It goes in there when it wants a nap," Paul said.

It was then I noticed a cat basket hanging in a corner of the shed and suddenly I had an idea! I'd take the cat to the hospital and show him to Mrs Thomas! That would really set her mind at rest.

He was eating the chicken so it was easy to get the basket down and slip him into it. But that's when things went wrong. You'd never believe how difficult it is to get on a bike trying to carry a cat basket with a struggling cat in it. Paul had gone in, thank goodness.

I had just managed to get on the bike when I heard a shout.

"Hey, what do you think you're doing with that cat?"

He was back!

"Well, I —" I nearly dropped the basket.

"Of all the mean things!" Paul exclaimed. "To steal an old lady's cat while she's in hospital!"

"I'm not stealing it," I said. "I'm taking it to show her." I was mad, too. No one had ever accused me of stealing before.

"She was worried about her cat. You never thought of letting her know it was all right, I suppose."

"I looked after it," he said. "I didn't think she would be as worried as all that."

Just then the cat jerked in the basket and I nearly fell off the bike again.

"How do you think you're going to take it up on that?" he said. "Here, wait a minute. I'll take you in the car. Hold on, I'll tell Dad. Dad!" he shouted.

His Dad came out of the house, looked at me and the cat and said, "Sure you'll be all right?"

"Of course I will," Paul answered.

"He has only just passed his test," his father informed me.

Paul looked mad again, so I said cheerfully, "That's all right then — as long as he didn't fail,"

and climbed into the back of the car.

It didn't take us long to get to the hospital. Paul said he would stay in the car while I went up with the cat. He was having a bit of a grin to himself. "You'll cop it if Sister finds out," he said. "Don't try to hide it. Walk as if it's a picnic basket or something."

So I walked smartly across the car park. As it was Sunday afternoon, there weren't many nurses about and I managed to slither into the ward. Visiting had already started, which was a help.

"Mrs Thomas," I whispered.

"Katy!" she said, "how nice of you to come."

"I've brought the cat," I whispered again.

"What?" Mrs Thomas looked amazed.

"I thought you'd like to see him."

"My dear girl. How did you manage it? Where is he?"

I showed her the basket. Her face was a picture.

"Is he all right?" she whispered.

"He's fine," I said.

He had kept very quiet up until now, and I hoped he would keep it up. I undid the lid and let him poke his head out a little way. Mrs Thomas stroked him and made crooning noises. I must admit I was a bit on edge. If Sister found out, it might be the last of St John's for me and I hadn't been to the theatre once yet, let alone a football match.

Mrs Thomas was still stroking Toby's head when I saw a woman coming towards us.

"Mary!"

Mrs Thomas looked up.

"Sylvia!" she said. "How nice to see you."

"I only heard today that you were in hospital," the woman said. "How are you now?"

"Much better. I'm going home on Tuesday."

She turned to me. "Did you hear that, Katy? I'm going home on Tuesday. This is my friend, Mrs Ferguson, by the way. Katy belongs to the St John Ambulance," she added, "and she's been very kind to me."

Mrs Ferguson smiled. "What made you join St John's then, Katy?" she asked.

I liked Mrs Ferguson, so I told her all about Gilbert and Sullivan and going to the theatre free.

She laughed. "I love Gilbert and Sullivan too," she said. "My husband has a lot to do with the theatre, doesn't he, Mary?"

Just then, Toby thought that no one was taking much notice of him and gave a loud yell.

"What on earth was that?" Mrs Ferguson nearly fell off her chair.

"It's Toby — my cat. Katy brought him along so that I could see him."

Mrs Ferguson's eyes were wide. I was busy pushing Toby's head back into the basket and doing up the lid.

"I must go, Mrs Thomas," I said. "I'll see you tomorrow and let you know how things are."

Toby let out another screech and I could see Sister at the end of the ward, so I dashed out of the side door and ran towards the car park where I could see Paul waving furiously.

Thankfully, everything went well. I saw Mrs Thomas the next day and she said that Sister had thought the screech was a chair being pushed back, and no one had enlightened her.

Two days later, I had a surprise — a letter from Mrs Ferguson, thanking me for being so kind to her friend. Enclosed was a card. Her husband was a Director of the theatre and on the card he had written "Allow the holder of this card in to the theatre free at any time, together with a friend." It was signed "S. J. Ferguson."

I was so excited. I hugged Mum then I hugged Dad, and told them they could come with me any time they liked.

The trouble is, I've had the card nearly six weeks now and I haven't had time to go myself. Mum and Dad have been twice.

I shall *never* give up St John's. It's ace! One evening in December, we took the disabled people in their wheelchairs to do their Christmas shopping. All the shops opened for them. It was great!

Pete and Jim are both learning to drive, so they're up at Paul's place a lot, chatting about cars. I go up, too, and call on Mrs Thomas. Her cat is no worse for his adventure, and neither is she.

THE END

PART 4

THE RED BOX OF DESTINY

THE old-fashioned telephone box had been a familiar sight in the High Street for many years — but it was decided that the time had come to replace it.

THIS TELEPHONE WILL SHORTLY BE REPLACED BY A MODERN VERSION. THIS IS IN ACCORDANCE WITH OUR POLICY. WE APOLOGISE FOR ANY...

Oh, it's a shame! Those new telephone kiosks have got no character. Not like the old red ones.

You're right. This old box is part of our town. I reckon we ought to protest. Tell 'em we want to keep *THIS* one!

Good idea. Let's organise a meeting in the community centre.

Things quickly got moving—

Please, Aunt Edna — can we rest for a minute? My arms ache.

Stop moaning, Carrie — or your *HEAD* will ache, where I'll belt it.

SAVE OUR BOX

Excuse me, I wonder if you'd sign my petition to save the old red telephone box?

Of course. Anything to help.

I've hurt my arm, and the dear girl insisted on carrying all my shopping.

If I didn't, Jasper would suffer — poor little pup.

114

Later, at the community centre—

Service with a smile — thanks, Carrie.

I may have a smile on my face in public, but inside I'm crying.

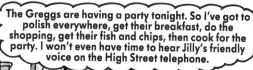

Early next Saturday, Carrie was set hard to work.

The Greggs are having a party tonight. So I've got to polish everywhere, get their breakfast, do the shopping, get their fish and chips, then cook for the party. I won't even have time to hear Jilly's friendly voice on the High Street telephone.

Much later—

Bring me some cocoa and biscuits in bed, then get this lot cleaned up. How'd the meeting go, so's I can seem interested if anyone asks?

They're having a protest rally round the phone box next Saturday. The local newspaper and TV are coming.

But, towards the end of that busy day—

I — I feel awful — so dizzy.

The poor lass has fainted!

Take Carrie and the pup out to the car, Jilly. And don't you dare, interfere—my husband is waiting outside. Carrie is coming home with *US!*

Later—

Thank you for your kindness — but why did you come round to the Greggs' house?

On the local lunchtime news, they mentioned the phone number of the old High Street box. I realised the number was the same as the 'home' one you'd given me.

Yes, and I thought there must be something wrong. You'd looked so tired on the occasions I'd seen you, so I decided to investigate. Luckily we came round when we did!

Your so-called 'family' will get their punishment, now we've called the authorities and told what we've seen. We'd like you to stay with us in the meantime — and if things work out, perhaps the arrangement could be permanent? Jasper too, of course!

Oh! It's wonderful! I can hardly believe it!

While Carrie's life was being turned upside down, Kelly Rees was still bitter. She too was attending the protest meeting.

I didn't know you were interested in the old telephone box, Kelly.

Why shouldn't I be?

Do you want me to stay with you?

No, thanks — but you will pick me up at nine o'clock, won't you?

I'm not really bothered about a stupid phone box — but Dad wanted to go to the snooker club tonight. Why should he be out enjoying himself, when HE was the one who stopped me dancing?

— and I don't think we should allow this piece of history to be taken away from us!

How much longer are people going to rabbit on?

Before we decide who'll do posters, petitions, and so on — there are refreshments being served at the kitchen counter.

About time!

EXCUSE ME! I find it difficult to get by with my sticks.

Oh, yes. I'm so sorry.

You'd think they'd let me to the front of the queue, being an invalid.

Kelly felt a push from behind, and—

Watch it! Can't you see that I'm an inv — OH!

Sorry. I was pretending my chair was a racing car again.

Hey, lay your sticks on my chair, get two cups of tea for me and Mum — and one for yourself — then you can hold on to my chair for support and we'll go back and sit down. Okay?

Um! I suppose so.

Soon—

Hi, Mum. I got some help. Sit down — er — what's your name? I'm David.

I'm Kelly Rees.

119

Oh! No biscuits? I'll get some for us. Beep-beep!

Careful! You'll be bowling someone over in that thing!

How long before you can do without your sticks, Kelly?

Never. Dad crashed the car, and this is as well as I'll get. It's not fair. Why me?

I asked myself "why David" — when he was struck down with a bone disease that stopped him from playing football, and running about like a normal little boy. Why SHOULD he have to endure treatment that gives him pain?

Oh, I — I'm sorry.

Don't let David hear you say that, Kelly. He says feeling sorry is daft — it doesn't help at all, just makes you feel worse.

Kelly chatted to David and his mother until the meeting recommenced.

Publicity posters? Kelly and I will make and deliver some — won't we, Kelly?

Well, er —

Well done, youngsters!

How can I deliver posters? I can only walk with sticks.

Easy. Dump them on my lap in my Batmobile, then you can support yourself and push *ME!*

In spite of herself, Kelly found David's enthusiasm infectious. To her surprise she enjoyed the Save Our Box campaign.

Shall I take you in the car?

That's a good idea, David?

No, the exercise will do us good. Now — forward charge!

Kelly arranged to meet David on the day of the protest rally outside the telephone box.

David and his Mum are late.

David's Mum came — alone.

Where's David? Isn't he well?

David — David had a sudden relapse, and died yesterday. I wanted to come and tell you myself.

Why? Why? It's just not fair!

Don't be bitter, Kelly. I'm not, because David would have hated that. He loved life, whether or not he was ill, and said there was no point in doing anything else but look on the bright side.

He was right. I'm ashamed of the way I've behaved. Before I destroy myself and my family with bitterness, I'll stop feeling sorry for myself — however hard it is, and no matter how long it takes.

A few days earlier, Rama Chand had also made a decision which was to change her life.

I've just *GOT* to go to the festival. I know Dad is going to be furious, but he doesn't understand how important music is to me.

I've arranged for one of the other waitresses to cover for me, so Dad won't be short-staffed at his special dinner tonight. I'll hurry to catch the coach, while he and Som are busy.

Don't look so nervous, Rama — I'm sure you'll make a very good impression in the musical.

122

Suddenly—

RAMA! Get off that coach immediately!

Dad!

When Shireen turned up to waitress, I insisted that she told me where you were. How dare you disobey me, Rama? Miss Ainsley, I am surprised that you encouraged her deceitfulness!

Miss Ainsley knew nothing about it, Dad — truly!

Please let her take part, Mr Chand. I'm sure we can sort something out?

NO! Come along, Rama.

Back in her room, Dad talked more kindly to Rama.

I don't want to seem harsh, Rama — but in the pop business, for every one who makes it to the top, hundreds don't. It's because I love you that I want you to have a secure future — here in the restaurant.

Two days later—

We'll go along to the protest meeting. It's good to be involved with the local community.

SAVE OUR BOX

Yes, Dad.

We need to draw public attention to the telephone box in some novel way. Any ideas?

Perhaps a song. I'm sure I could compose one, if Dad would agree.

A song? Of course. I don't want you to stop enjoying music altogether — but you must learn to keep it in perspective.

So, at the protest rally—

♫ It isn't just a box to us, ♪
Tired and faded red,
So don't you tear its heart out,
And leave it cold and dead —

SAVE OUR BOX

Watching the lunchtime news, someone took a great interest in Rama's singing—

The reporter said this girl composed the words and music herself. I've a feeling she's got real talent. We must contact her.

Later that day—

A recording test? No, Mr Sanders. Rama knows her future is to be in the family business, and not in music.

Why not combine the two? I'm sure your diners would appreciate beautiful singing to go with their delicious food.

At last Mr Chand agreed to let Rama go to the recording studios, on condition that he escorted her himself.

She really lives and breathes the music.

Yes. I must admit I've never seen her looking so happy. But I only want what's best for her.

Mr Chand, how would you feel if you were told you could never again create your wonderful dishes? That you must never cook any more?

I'd be devastated. Cooking is my way of life.

Rama's father realised what Mr Sanders meant.

Perhaps I've been wrong. Rama is so happy singing, it would be cruel to deprive her of her music.

And to Rama's joy—

Mr Sanders has recommended a reputable music school. You may attend during term time, to study music — but during the holidays you must get a proper grounding in the family business, in case your music career doesn't succeed.

Oh, thank you — thank you, Dad!

A few days after the protest rally, it was announced that the telephone box would be saved. Three girls looked at it, each with her own special reason for being grateful.

TELEPHONE TELEPHONE

I've a new home and family, thanks to the old telephone box.

I helped to save the telephone box from being destroyed — and it has helped me to carry on with my music. Thanks, old friend.

Flowers for David's grave. If it hadn't been for the phone box, I'd never have met him, and changed my life.

THE END

Look, Patch — this book is all I need
To work out just what's in your breed!

St Bernard dog, with nose so keen —
Finding lost travellers is HIS scene.

When WE went out, in snow and frost,
I might have known that YOU'D get lost!

Big and tough and bold and strong,
The Husky pulls a sledge along.

But when I tried it out with you,
Guess who finished pulling WHO?